PRECIOUS MOMENTS™

Precious Nursery Rhymes

Rhymes adapted & Illustrated by Samuel J. Butcher

Old Mother Hubbard

Went to the cupboard

To get her poor puppy a bone.

So she said a short prayer

Before she got there.

And, praise the Lord,

There was one!

Hey, diddle, diddle,

The cat and the fiddle,

The cow jumped over the moon.

But the cat didn't worry

Because Bossy hurried

To make it back home very soon.

winkle,
twinkle, little star,
Oh, how lovely you are.
God created you to shine
Like a diamond for all time.

ittle Bo Peep

Takes care of her sheep

And always knows

   where to find them.

Her sheep never roam

Too far from their home,

For Bo Peep is always

   behind them.

here was an old lady
Who lived in a shoe.
She had so many children,
She didn't know what to do.
So she asked God to help her
And show His great love
By blessing her house
With His help from above.

Jack, be nimble.
Jack, be quick.
Jack, jump over
   the candlestick.
Because to jump and exercise
Will make you healthy,
   strong, and wise.

ary, Mary,

So extraordinary,

How does your garden grow?

With plenty of love,

And rain from above,

That's how my dear

garden grows.

Old King Cole

Was a merry old soul.

A merry old soul was he,

Because he was blessed

With good friends and success

In a kingdom of pure harmony.

Rub-a-dub-dub,

Three men in a tub

Sailed away

on the ocean blue.

But they weren't afraid

Because they all made

A great team

and a wonderful crew.

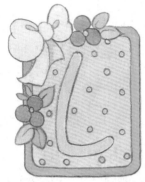ittle Miss Muffet

Sat on her tuffet,

And then she started to pray:

Dear Lord, there's a spidee

Who's sitting beside me.

Please ask it to just go away!

ittle Boy Blue,

Come blow your horn.

The sheep's in the meadow,

The cow's in the corn.

And where is Boy Blue,

Who is faithful each day?

He still has his horn

And is now on his way.

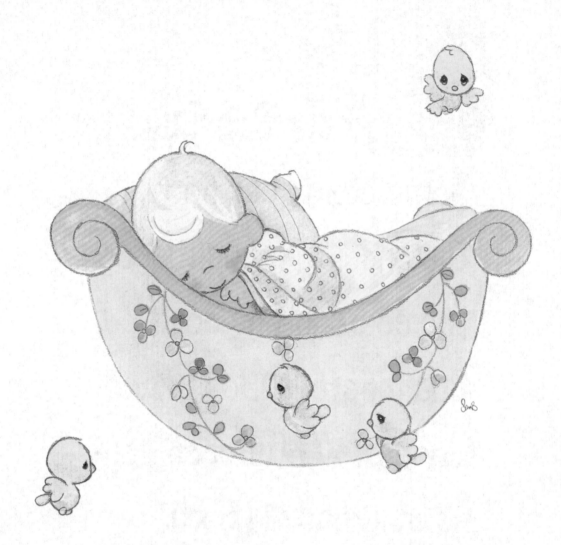